YOU KNOW YOU'RE

60

WHEN...

The Quiz of Your Lifetime

Mike Haskins

Illustrations by Ian Baker

summersdale

YOU KNOW YOU'RE 60 WHEN...

An Hachette UK Company
www.hachette.co.uk

Summersdale Publishers Ltd
Part of Octopus Publishing Group Limited
Carmelite House
50 Victoria Embankment
LONDON
EC4Y 0DZ
UK

www.summersdale.com

Printed and bound in Malta

ISBN: 978-1-78685-541-1

TO...

FROM...

INTRODUCTION

WOW! YOU'RE 60! CONGRATULATIONS!

Age 60 used to be so old. At least, that's the way it seemed when you were young. But things have changed since then. Being 60 today isn't anything like what it used to be. If you're 60 today, you look and feel nowhere near as old as someone who was 60 when you were born. And no, that's not because they're now 120.

The 60-year-olds of today have more to look forward to than ever before. They are better off, fitter, more active and better-looking. Well, some 60-year-olds are. Many even have more energy than 20-year-olds, although that's probably because the 20-year-olds have worn themselves out doing the things that 20-year-olds like to get up to.

But perhaps, most importantly, 60-year-olds are filled with experience – hopefully about 60 years' worth!

As a 60-year-old, you have lived through some of the most extraordinary and dramatic events in human history. No wonder you look the way you do.

Unfortunately, you may not remember the great historic events of your lifetime in as much detail as the sweets you gorged yourself on or the toys you played with when you were little, or the pop songs and adverts that have been floating around in your head for over half a century.

And that's where this little quiz volume comes in. You've lived through 60 long years and now you can test yourself to see what you can remember about them. But don't worry if the answers don't immediately spring to mind, because you can just turn the page after each quiz, look at the answers and revel in the nostalgic glow of it all. It wouldn't really be cheating, it would just be a handy way to remind yourself about some of the things you've lived through over the last 60 magnificent years.

YOU KNOW YOU'RE 60 WHEN...

YOU REMEMBER WHEN SWEETS COST 6D

Chocolate bars and tubes of sweets only cost the equivalent of 2.5 pence when you were little, and yet it seemed like your mum and dad rarely allowed you to have them. Today, you could buy them for yourself, even though they cost about 3,000 per cent more. Unfortunately, you're also now aware just how bad they are for you. So, instead of eating them, let's see if you can at least remember the following delicacies from your youth.

1. The words 'Desperation, Pacification, Expectation, Acclamation, Realization' were printed on the wrapper of which chocolate bar?

2. Which chocolate bar featured individual segments that were Turkish Delight, Almond Whirl, Orange Cream, Fudge, Cokernut Ice, Lime Cordial, Caramel, Creme Strawberry and Coffee Creme?

3. Which sweets came in the following varieties: original, acid drop, blackcurrant and Old English?

4. Can you complete the advertising slogan: 'Don't forget the ...'?

5. Which classic 1960s bar featured chocolate, nougatine and caramel, and was advertised on TV in the setting of a South American temple?

6. Which toffee and chocolate bar was advertised by Terry Scott dressed in a schoolboy's uniform?

7   The advert for which bar claimed: 'It's got two kinds of chocolate and caramel too! And it's got raisins and they're good for you!'

8   Which chocolate bar was advertised with the warning: 'Don't 'ee knock it all back at once!'

9   Which was the sweet you could eat between meals without ruining your appetite?

10   Which chocolate was claimed to be exotic, delicious and full of Eastern promise?

YOU KNOW YOU'RE 60 WHEN...

YOU REMEMBER WHEN SWEETS COST 6D
— ANSWERS —

1 The words appeared on the wrappers for Fry's Five Boys Chocolate, beneath the mugshots of five urchins (or perhaps the same urchin experiencing five different states of choc-driven emotion) apparently photographed some time during the Edwardian era. Hopefully that didn't make people think the chocolate was past its use-by date.

2 Milk Tray. Yes, in your younger days they did it in a bar as well as in a box, and 'cokernut' really was spelt like that. And how cruel to have Coffee Creme as one of the centres. That was probably the one you left for your dad!

3 Spangles. Those were, of course, just some of the tempting flavours of the nostalgia buff's favourite sweet, which was available from the 1950s through to 1984.

4 'Don't forget the Fruit Gums, mum!' (Or sometimes 'Don't forget the Fruit Gums, chum!') Rowntree's Fruit Gums were quite hard and needed some work to chew down. Perhaps it would have been better to tell mum: 'Don't forget to book a check-up at the dentist!'

5 Aztec Bar. The Aztec people may have discovered chocolate over a thousand years ago, but, sadly, Aztec bars didn't last quite so long, being launched in 1967 and discontinued in 1978.

6 Curly Wurly. In the early 1970s, Terry Scott, then in his mid forties, warned everyone off with a cry of 'Hands off my Curly Wurly!' He did so in the same schoolboy character he had played on his 1962 hit 'My Brother'. In real life, Terry admitted to enjoying a life of 'booze, fags and birds', which ultimately did his health no favours. He should have stuck to the Curly Wurlys!

7   Amazin' Raisin Bar. The jingle claimed:
    'It's amazin' what raisins can do!' But
    were small dried fruits genuinely
    capable of doing anything amazin'?

8   Old Jamaica. In the ads, a pirate character
    warned children not to knock it all back
    at once, as though this rum-and-raisin-
    flavoured bar was 40 per cent proof!

9   Milky Way. We were regularly told we could
    eat these between meals without ruining
    our appetite. Surely this couldn't be true if
    you spent the entire period between meals
    stuffing yourself with Milky Way bars?

10 Fry's Turkish Delight was full of Eastern
    promise, although this didn't seem to be
    listed as one of the ingredients on the side
    of the rectangular packet. And is it really
    the same size today as it used to be?

YOU KNOW YOU'RE 60 WHEN...

EVENTS FROM ANCIENT HISTORY OCCURRED WHEN YOU WERE AT PRIMARY SCHOOL

You grew up in momentous times. There was cultural upheaval and there were high-profile crimes and assassinations, wars, protests, scandals and drugs. None of that may have been reported in your weekly copy of *Playhour* comic, but can you answer the following about the events of your early life?

1. Who was the Secretary of State for War who resigned on 5 June 1963?

2. Which group, who found fame in August 1963, included Bruce Reynolds, Buster Edwards and Ronnie Biggs?

3. Who went to the seaside over a bank holiday in 1964 but ended up in a fight?

4. Why did The Beatles go to Buckingham Palace on 26 October 1965?

5. Complete the following list of football scores from July 1966: Uruguay 0–0; Mexico 2–0; France 2–0; Argentina 1–0; Portugal 2–1.

6. Which Caroline connected Tony Blackburn, Johnnie Walker, Dave Lee Travis, Emperor Rosko and Simon Dee?

7. What was the name of the boat in which Francis Chichester sailed around the world in nine months and a day, having set off from Plymouth on 27 August 1966?

8   Carole Hersee and Bubbles the Clown
    appeared on television for the first time
    on 2 July 1967. What were they doing?
    If you want a clue, they didn't move
    very much.

9   What royal event occurred at
    Caernarfon Castle on 1 July 1969?

10 What were the names of the three
    astronauts who crewed the Apollo 11
    mission in July 1969? And in which
    year were they all born?

YOU KNOW YOU'RE 60 WHEN...

EVENTS FROM ANCIENT HISTORY OCCURRED WHEN YOU WERE AT PRIMARY SCHOOL

— ANSWERS —

1 John Profumo. The Profumo scandal came to light almost two years after Profumo's affair with then 19-year-old Christine Keeler, who had also been in a relationship with a Soviet naval attaché. So perhaps it was Profumo who really kick-started the swinging sixties?

2 The Great Train Robbers. Despite being a group of criminals not a pop group, some were also guilty of crimes against music. Ronnie Biggs appeared on a single with the Sex Pistols in 1978. And Buster Edwards was indirectly responsible for Phil Collins doing 'Groovy Kind of Love', as featured in the 1988 biopic *Buster*.

3 Mods and Rockers. Over the 1964 Whitsun bank holiday weekend, scores of youths fought it out in Brighton, Hastings and other seaside towns to establish which of them liked the best music and combed their hair the correct way!

4 The Fab Four went to Buckingham Palace to receive their MBEs from Her Majesty the Queen. It was also alleged they shared a joint while they were there, although that isn't usually part of the ceremony.

5 West Germany 4–2. The other scores were from the earlier rounds of England's path to World Cup glory.

6 The DJs all broadcast for pirate radio station Radio Caroline. Caroline did not, however, seem a particularly chilling pirate name, at least not compared to Long John Silver or Blackbeard.

7. *Gipsy Moth IV*. Back in the 1960s, it was possible for a 65-year-old man smoking a pipe to become a great English sporting hero. He was knighted halfway round his trip, which rarely happens with sportsmen who compete in shorter events like the 100 metres.

8. Carole played noughts and crosses with her toy Bubbles on the BBC test card, which appeared on screen for an estimated 70,000 hours over the following 30 years. Despite this, the noughts and crosses game never progressed very far.

9. The investiture of Prince Charles as Prince of Wales. Her Majesty the Queen crowned her son Prince of Wales shortly after he had finished his second year at university. Some of us just get given a book token.

10. Neil Armstrong, Buzz Aldrin and Michael Collins. And all of them were born in 1930, just 27 years after the Wright brothers' first-ever flight.

YOU KNOW YOU'RE 60 WHEN...

YOU STILL YEARN FOR YOUR CHILDHOOD TOYS FROM 50 YEARS AGO

Nothing was more precious to you when you were little than your toys. And that's why you spent years gradually bashing them to smithereens. Now, of course, you can buy them all again as new on eBay from oddballs who never played with their toys or even took them out of their boxes. But how much do you remember about your old toys?

1. The Barbie doll was first introduced in 1959. But what is Barbie's full name? And what are the names of her boyfriend and her 14-year-old sister'?

2. Who was Barbie's British rival? And who was that rival doll's boyfriend and little sister?

3. Action Man was launched in the UK in 1966 as the British equivalent of the American G. I. Joe action figure. What were the first three different types of Action Man available? And what was the name of his rival in the British market at that time?

4. Corgi issued a toy car model of the Aston Martin DB5 featured in the 1964 James Bond film *Goldfinger*. What three special 'top secret' features did the car possess?

5. What toy launched in the UK in 1965 by Denys Fisher promised 'pattern drawing by revolving stencils'?

6   Which game launched by MB Games in 1966 promised to 'tie you up in knots'?

7   Which plastic dolls were created by Danish woodcutter Thomas Dam in the early 1960s and often had a shock of brightly coloured hair?

8   What was the magic screen advertised as 'fun for all the family'?

9   Which modelling clay had originally been created to clean wallpaper?

10 Which world-beating toy from Denmark was first seen in the UK at the Brighton Toy Fair in 1960?

YOU KNOW YOU'RE 60 WHEN...

YOU STILL YEARN FOR YOUR CHILDHOOD TOYS FROM 50 YEARS AGO

— ANSWERS —

1. Barbie's full name is Barbara Millicent Roberts. Her boyfriend is Ken and her 14-year-old sister is Skipper.

2. Sindy was the British rival to Barbie. Her boyfriend is Paul and her little sister is Patch. For some reason, the younger sisters of famous dolls always seem to have names that sound like they should be given to pets rather than humans!

3. Soldier, sailor and pilot, although you'd think a tinker and a tailor version of Action Man might have made a more complete set alongside the

soldier and sailor. The competitor action figure in the British market was Tommy Gunn, who sadly laid down his arms after just two years in 1968.

4 Machine guns that popped out of the front bumper; a bulletproof screen that rose up out of the boot; and, of course, the ejector seat that launched a little plastic baddy out through the sunroof. Forget heated seats or satnavs, these are the extras every 60-year-old wants on his or her new car.

5 Spirograph. This toy comprised a box full of little plastic cogs that you could use to draw intricate geometrical patterns until you had completely obliterated your piece of paper with pencil or ink.

6 Twister. When the game was demonstrated on US television on 3 May 1966 by chat-show host Johnny Carson and his guest Eva Gabor, there was concern about the potential immorality offered by what was described as 'sex in a box'. People should have been more concerned about the potential for putting your back out instead!

7 Troll dolls or gonk trolls. With their shock of pink, orange, blue, yellow, purple or green hair and wrinkled faces, these looked like normal dolls who had reached old age and decided to become hippies!

8 Etch A Sketch. This proved a hugely popular toy in the 1960s, even though it provided a significantly less efficient way of drawing than using a pencil and a piece of paper.

9 Play-Doh. You could mould it, shape it, feed it through a plastic mincer or just sit there sniffing the irresistible smell that arose from the Play-Doh tub.

10 It was, of course, the plastic building bricks of Lego. Despite their huge popularity, few people used Lego to build themselves full-size houses which they could take apart and re-assemble as a car to drive to work in the morning.

YOU KNOW YOU'RE 60 WHEN...

YOUR HEAD IS FULL OF OLD ADVERTISING SLOGANS

Today, TV commercials look like Hollywood movies and advertise cars, mobile phone contracts or what to do if you've had an accident that wasn't your fault. When you were young, ads were for the most basic everyday products, often filmed in someone's kitchen, and had the most annoying jingles known to man. And yet they were so much more fun! Can you complete the following slogans and identify which products they advertised?

1. '... Central heating for kids.'
2. '... Naughty but nice.'
3. 'Graded grains ...'
4. 'A million housewives every day ...'
5. 'Now hands that do dishes can feel ...'
6. 'Let your fingers ...'
7. 'And all because ...'
8. 'Go to work on ...'
9. 'For mash ...'
10. 'Lipsmackin' thirstquenchin' ...'

YOU KNOW YOU'RE 60 WHEN...

YOUR HEAD IS FULL OF OLD ADVERTISING SLOGANS

— ANSWERS —

1. 'Ready Brek...' The TV ads featured children with a glowing halo all around their bodies, as though their breakfast bowl of Ready Brek cereal had been radioactive. All mums and dads needed to do was serve a bowl of piping-hot Ready Brek and they could use their kids to heat their house.

2. 'Fresh cream cakes...' A slogan for the Milk Marketing Board penned by a young Salman Rushdie. He also came up with 'That'll do nicely' for American Express, and 'Irresistibubble',

'Delectabubble' and 'Adorabubble' for Aero, all of which got him into considerably less trouble than some of his later work!

3 '... make finer flour.' Work apparel at the Homepride Flour factory for some reason comprised a suit and bowler hat, and all the workers sounded like John le Mesurier from *Dad's Army*.

4 '... pick up a tin of beans and say, Beanz Meanz Heinz!' However, no one ever asked Heinz for the details of these million housewives to check that they really did do this every day.

5 '... as soft as your face with mild green Fairy Liquid.' A more efficient way to keep your hands soft was to wear rubber gloves.

6 '... do the walking.' If you were too lazy to walk to the shops, you could use Yellow Pages and let your fingers do the walking. These days, people are too lazy to walk as far as their copy of Yellow Pages and let their fingers do the walking on their smartphones instead.

7 ... the lady loves Milk Tray.' This slogan was used in a long-running series of ads in which a James Bond-like figure risked his life to deliver boxes of Milk Tray chocolates in perilous conditions.

8 '... an egg.' A 1960s slogan penned by another future literary name, Fay Weldon. Eggs are not, however, a recommended form of transport to get to work or to anywhere else.

9 '... get Smash.' The adverts for this instant mashed potato depicted metal aliens who deduced the ignorance of the human race through our habit of peeling and boiling potatoes before smashing them all to bits.

10 '... acetastin' motivatin' goodbuzzin' cooltalkin' highwalkin' fastlivin' evergivin' coolfizzin' Pepsi.' A slogan that is both highly memorable and completely impossible to remember at the same time!

YOU KNOW YOU'RE 60 WHEN...

YOUR FAVOURITE KIDS' TV SHOWS ARE FROM 50 YEARS AGO

You may struggle to remember all the names of your old teachers and school friends, but you probably have no trouble remembering the names of every character in the TV shows you sat glued to on your parents' old black-and-white TV set. See how you do on the following.

1. Can you name three places that lay in the county of Trumptonshire?

2. Which series, translated from the original French, told the adventures of a boy and his Pyrenean Mountain Dog in the French Alps?

3. In the TV series *The Herbs*, what sort of animals were Parsley, Dill, Sage and Tarragon?

4. Which cartoon series featured the Gruesome Twosome in the Creepy Coupe, Lazy Luke and Blubber Bear in the Arkansas Chugabug, and Peter Perfect in the Turbo Terrific?

5. Which series featured Brains, Billie, Sticks, Scooper, Spring, Doughnut and Tiger?

6. The main characters of which puppet series were a dog, a cat and a frog?

7. Which cartoon series featured Benny the Ball, Fancy-Fancy, Spook and Brain?

8. Who lived at 52 Festive Road and mainly seemed to leave his house to visit a nearby fancy-dress shop?

YOU KNOW YOU'RE 60 WHEN...

YOUR FAVOURITE KIDS' TV SHOWS ARE FROM 50 YEARS AGO
— ANSWERS —

1 Camberwick Green, Trumpton and Chigley

As featured in the *Watch with Mother* trilogy first broadcast in 1966, 1967 and 1969 respectively. Characters included Windy Miller, Mrs Honeyman, Dr Mopp, Chippy Minton and the firefighters Pugh, Pugh, Barney McGrew, Cuthbert, Dibble and Grubb. Unusually for an English county, Trumptonshire only seemed to contain three places in total.

2 Belle and Sebastian

A black-and-white series filmed in French and dubbed into English in 1967. It told the story of an orphan boy and his dog in the French Alps, but not their adventures in the 1990s when they formed an indie band in Glasgow.

3 Parsley was a lion, Dill a dog, Sage an owl and Tarragon a dragon.

The Herbs was an animated series first broadcast in 1968 and created by author Michael Bond, who, apparently after creating Paddington Bear, went on to draw inspiration from the herb and spice rack in his kitchen!

4 Wacky Races

First broadcast by the BBC in 1969. The series, of course, also featured Penelope Pitstop in the Compact Pussycat, the Ant Hill Mob in the Bulletproof Bomb and Dick Dastardly and Muttley in the Mean Machine.

5 Here Come the Double Deckers

Broadcast in 1971 and 1972, Spring was played by Brinsley Forde, later of reggae band Aswad, and Scooper was played by Peter Firth, later of the TV series Spooks.

6 Hector's House

First shown in the UK in 1968, having been translated into English, this French series seemed to involve a bizarre ménage à trois that crossed the animal and, indeed, amphibian divide.

7 Top Cat

Benny the Ball was voiced by Maurice Gosfield, essentially repeating his role of Private Doberman in Sergeant Bilko. During the 1960s and 1970s, the BBC tried to fool us into believing the show was called Boss Cat to stop us rushing out to buy the unrelated Top Cat brand of cat food available at the time.

8 Mr Benn

This classic animated series created by David McKee, who also gave us King Rollo and Elmer the Elephant, was transmitted in 1971 and 1972 and told the adventures of a bowler-hatted gent who seemed to have a thing about dressing up in unusual costumes.

YOU KNOW YOU'RE 60 WHEN...

YOU LAST GOT INTO THE CINEMA AT HALF PRICE HALF A CENTURY AGO

Going to the cinema was a big event when you were little. You looked forward for weeks to the day you would be taken to the local cinema, where you would experience a magical once in a lifetime chance to see the latest big new film. Luckily, they are now all constantly repeated on TV, so you should have no problem remembering the following films of your youth.

1. In Disney's 1967 animation *The Jungle Book*, what animals were Baloo, Bagheera, King Louie, Kaa, Shere Khan and Colonel Hathi?

2. Which 1967 musical film featured animals that included Polynesia the parrot, Chee-Chee the chimpanzee, Jip the dog and a pushmi-pullyu, and a human character who was able to talk to them?

3. Which 1968 film musical featured Caractacus Potts, Truly Scrumptious and the Child Catcher?

4. Which Dickensian hero dreamed of 'hot sausage and mustard' and 'cold jelly and custard' in a 1968 film musical?

5. What cartoon cat had the first names Abraham de Lacy Giuseppe Casey? Try singing it if you're not sure!

6 What did Augustus Gloop, Veruca Salt, Violet Beauregarde, Mike Teavee and Charlie Bucket have in common in 1971?

7 In the 1970 film *The Railway Children*, what did sisters Bobbie and Phyllis use as signals to save the 11.29 train from crashing into a landslide across the line?

8 In which 1971 film were three children evacuated from London to live with a woman who was doing a correspondence course in witchcraft?

9 In which 1973 Arabian Nights adventure did Tom Baker play Prince Koura, who brings a six-armed statue of the goddess Kali to life?

10 Which 1973 animation was narrated by a singing cockerel?

YOU KNOW YOU'RE 60 WHEN...

YOU LAST GOT INTO THE CINEMA AT HALF PRICE HALF A CENTURY AGO

— ANSWERS —

1 Baloo was a sloth bear, Bagheera a panther, King Louie an orangutan, Kaa a python, Shere Khan a Bengal tiger and Colonel Hathi an Indian elephant. Presumably King Louie and the other orangutans had come over on holiday from Borneo to India at the time the story took place.

2 *Doctor Dolittle*, the story of a man who learned to talk to the animals and from whom Johnny Morris presumably learnt everything he knew for *Animal Magic*.

3   *Chitty Chitty Bang Bang.* The musical version of the children's book by Ian Fleming which, like the James Bond movies, featured a car capable of doing many extraordinary things.

4   Oliver in *Oliver!* The sight of the thin, grey gruel served up in the workhouse scene was as terrifying to us when we were children as any adult horror film.

5   Thomas O'Malley in Disney's *The Aristocats.* O'Malley was the alley cat who helps Duchess and her kittens after they are kidnapped by their mistress' evil butler.

6   They were the children who won golden tickets in *Willie Wonka and the Chocolate Factory.* The film, based on Roald Dahl's book, told the terrifying story of a madman who tempts boys and girls into his mysterious factory, where one by one they meet their doom!

7   Their red bloomers. These days, they would just have been given a fine for trespassing on the line.

8   *Bedknobs and Broomsticks.* Angela Lansbury played Eglantine Price in the Disney magical adventure that combined live action and animation, but which wasn't *Mary Poppins.*

9 *The Golden Voyage of Sinbad*. The goddess Kali was the work of animation genius Ray Harryhausen.

10 Disney's version of *Robin Hood*, which featured 'King of the Road' singer Roger Miller as Alan-a-Dale, Peter Ustinov as both King Richard and Prince John, and Terry-Thomas as Sir Hiss (a character few remember from the original Robin Hood stories!).

YOU KNOW YOU'RE 60 WHEN...

YOU STILL REGARD THINGS FROM THE 1960s AND 1970s AS 'NEW TECHNOLOGY'

In the 1960s technology put a man on the Moon. Today we all have more computer power than was available to Neil Armstrong in our phones and use it to watch funny films about cats and to tell people when we have got on trains. But let's think back to the days when technology was more basic and yet more exciting.

1. Which supersonic aircraft developed jointly by the UK and France made its maiden flight on 2 March 1969?

2. Which product got its name after it was used in the Houston Astrodome sports stadium in 1966?

3. Which device was first demonstrated at the Enfield branch of Barclays Bank by *On the Buses* comedy star Reg Varney in June 1967?

4. The handheld electronic calculator was invented in 1967 and marketed in the 1970s. But which number did you have to type in to make the word 'boobies'?

5. Speaking of which, in 1962 Texan housewife Timmie Jean Lindsey was the first person to have which cosmetic surgical procedure?

6. Which product was introduced by Philips in Europe in 1963 and went on to 'kill music' in the 1970s?

7 Which item of stationery often used to colour in the front of school exercise books was invented by Yukio Horie of the Tokyo Stationery Company in 1960s?

8 Which musical instrument was invented by Dr Robert A. Moog in 1964?

9 Which electronic, labour-saving kitchen utensil was first demonstrated in Paris in 1971 by Pierre Verdon?

10 Which household safety device was invented in 1969 by Randolph Smith and Kenneth House?

YOU KNOW YOU'RE 60 WHEN...

YOU STILL REGARD THINGS FROM THE 1960s AND 1970s AS 'NEW TECHNOLOGY'

— ANSWERS —

1 *Concorde*, the Anglo-French supersonic aircraft capable of cruising at twice the speed of sound. At last, an aeroplane was designed to look like the planes we used to make out of sheets of paper.

2 Astroturf, now popular as a form of grass toupee for your garden. It means you don't have to mow your grass, but you do have to spend just as long going over it with the vacuum cleaner before putting it in the washing machine to get the stains out.

3 Two years before starring in *On The Buses*, when he was famous for shows like *The Rag Trade* and *Beggar My Neighbour*, cheeky cockney comedy actor Reg Varney demonstrated the world's first cash machine. A large crowd gathered to watch the demonstration, all of whom presumably found out Reg's PIN.

4 The number you needed to put into your calculator before turning it upside down to reveal the word 'boobies' was '5318008'. Coincidentally, this was also Reg Varney's cashpoint card PIN.

5 Mrs Lindsey was fitted with the world's first silicone breast implants. It was no surprise that it was a couple of men, Frank Gerow and Thomas Cronin, who came up with the idea and performed the operation!

6 The audio cassette. In the 1970s, you were warned that 'home taping' was killing music. That was because you were using cassettes to make muffled, warbly copies of your favourite songs off the Sunday-night chart rundown on Radio 1, all of which ended with the first few syllables of the DJ beginning to say something.

7 Yukio Horie developed the fibre-tip or felt-tip pen. Over the course of your childhood, you probably amassed hundreds of these things in every imaginable colour, about three of which seemed to work properly.

8 Moog invented the synthesizer and so indirectly gave us prog-rock in the 1970s, electro in the 1980s and techno in the early 1990s. Presumably at his funeral, in 2005, the music played involved a mix of Emerson, Lake and Palmer, Gloria Gaynor and Aphex Twin.

9 The food processor, although Verdon's device was called Le Magi-Mix – 1971 is also believed to be the date that a food processor was first put in the back of a kitchen cupboard never to be used again.

10 The battery-powered smoke alarm, a brilliant device if you want a loud beep to alert you every time you try to make a piece of toast. But they can prove dangerous if fire breaks out and the batteries have run down as a result of going off every time you made toast.

YOU KNOW YOU'RE 60 WHEN...

YOU'RE STILL HAUNTED BY THOSE SCARY PUBLIC INFORMATION FILMS

The 1970s gave us some classic works of horror, including *The Exorcist*, *The Omen* and *The Texas Chainsaw Massacre*. But perhaps the most chilling and widely seen of all were the public information safety films that would crop up on TV during the adverts while you were trying to watch *Magpie* or *The Tomorrow People*. Can you complete the following important yet terrifying messages?

1. 'I am the spirit of ...'

2. 'Stand still. Stand steady. ...'

3. 'Always use the Green Cross Code because ...'

4. 'Charley says ...'

5. 'Polish a floor and put a rug on it. ...'

6. 'When you fly your kite or model plane, ...'

7. 'Think once! Think twice! ...'

8. 'It can happen anywhere to anyone. An ordinary street, ...'

9. 'The last place in the world to leave a bottle ...'

10. 'Don't be an amber gambler, ...'

YOU KNOW YOU'RE 60 WHEN...

YOU'RE STILL HAUNTED BY THOSE SCARY PUBLIC INFORMATION FILMS

— ANSWERS —

1   '... dark and lonely water.'

Truly a mini-horror classic, in which the chilling tones of Donald Pleasance warned 'the unwary, the show-off, the fool' about the dangers of messing about near water. Clearly, if you wanted to summon up this ghostly monk-like apparition, the way to do it was to use a flimsy twig to try and retrieve a football from an unexpectedly deep puddle.

2 '... Stand clear.'

An ad which warned about the dangers of escalators by showing a child's wellington boot being horrifically mangled when it got too near the side. Obviously, most importantly of all, you should never ride on an escalator while wearing wellies!

3 '... I won't be there when you cross the road.'

The Green Cross Code Man (played by Bristol-born, future-Darth Vader Dave Prowse) was a superhero whose incredible power was knowing how to cross the road safely.

4 '... never go anywhere with men or ladies you don't know.'

In fact, Charley the cartoon cat told his little boy owner many important things, including 'always tell your mummy before you go off somewhere, so she knows who you are with' and 'if ever you see a box of matches lying around, tell mummy because they can hurt you'. However, Charley never thought to ask mummy why she kept leaving her child with only a cat to look after him!

5 '... You might as well set a mantrap.'

This ad featured a proud new grandma
polishing her house to welcome her son and
daughter-in-law and their newborn baby home
from the hospital. Grandma and mum's faces
froze in horror as dad went flying after stepping
on the rug in the hallway. 'And to think – he'd
only just come from the hospital!' Presumably a
moment later, despite the poor man's injuries,
mum and grandma were nevertheless wetting
themselves laughing.

6 '... remember you're in charge of a
flying machine.'

In this advert a small boy was frazzled before our
eyes after deciding to fly his kite right next to a
massive electricity pylon.

7 '... Think bike!'

This film warned car drivers to watch out for
motorbikes at junctions and made its impact
by graphically showing a collision before actor
Edward Judd concluded the ad by karate-
chopping the desk at which he was sitting
(and possibly going on to head-butt it for
good measure).

8 '... a moment's thoughtlessness.'

At which point, a man, clearly too engrossed in the newspaper he has just purchased, walks straight in front of a moving car. To make the point even more dramatically, we were then shown a peach being obliterated by a hammer. Whatever you do, don't eat peaches near anyone working with hammers!

9 '... is a beach!'

Another terrifying ad which featured a little boy, this time left on his own at the seaside to run around endlessly for no apparent reason – until, that is, the final chilling freeze-frame showing his foot about to embed itself on a jagged, broken lemonade bottle!

10 '... you might not be the only one around.'

In this film, a spiv character risked going through the traffic lights just as they were changing, only to crash into a car apparently being driven by his identical twin brother! Presumably lots of people disregarded this advice because they didn't have twin brothers.

YOU KNOW YOU'RE 60 WHEN...

YOU WISH *JUNIOR CHOICE* WAS STILL ON THE RADIO

In the good old days, *Junior Choice* was a Saturday-morning radio show which played kids' favourite fun songs. Today the same thing would probably consist of two hours of expletive-laden hip hop and hard rock. Perhaps they should start a show called *Senior Choice*, featuring the following records which were popular when you were a junior.

1. Which Bernard Cribbins' 1962 hit told the tale of a group of workmen trying to shift a piano?

2. Which 1966 Beatles hit begins 'In the town where I was born'?

3. In 1968, who implored us to 'drink a drink a drink to Lily the Pink the Pink the Pink'? And what exactly was it that she had invented?

4. What did Ohio Express claim to have in their tummy in 1968?

5. What three types of joyful commemoration are mentioned in the chorus of Cliff Richard's 1968 Eurovision Song Contest entry?

6. What did Lee Marvin claim he was born under in his 1969 hit song?

7 What three types of sweet substances are mentioned in the chorus of the 1969 hit by The Archies?

8 Which silent-film comedy star is mentioned in Clive Dunn's 1971 number one 'Grandad'?

9 Which 1970 number one began 'You could hear the hoof beats pound as they raced across the ground'? And which future UK prime minister chose it as one of his Desert Island Discs in 2006?

10 Which product had the New Seekers' 1972 hit song 'I'd Like to Teach the World To Sing' previously been used to advertise?

YOU KNOW YOU'RE 60 WHEN...

YOU WISH *JUNIOR CHOICE* WAS STILL ON THE RADIO

— ANSWERS —

1   'Right Said Fred'. Thirty years later, in 1992, the title was nabbed by a band of bald bodybuilders, but it was originally the great actor, comedian and future voice of *The Wombles*, Bernard Cribbins, who was too sexy for his shirt.

2   'Yellow Submarine', the only Beatles' single to spawn not only a hit film, but also a die-cast Corgi Toy model.

3 The Scaffold (featuring Paul McCartney's brother Mike) had a Christmas number one with 'Lily the Pink', who was 'the saviour of the human race, for she invented medicinal compound, most efficacious in every case'.

4 Ohio Express had love in their tummy, which does sound a little bit disgusting!

5 Cliff experienced 'congratulations', 'jubilations' and 'celebrations' in his 1968 Eurovision entry. Unfortunately, he didn't win, so the disappointing result possibly caused 'palpitations', 'exasperations' and 'exclamations'!

6 Lee Marvin was, of course, born under a 'Wand'rin Star' in the hit song from the musical *Paint Your Wagon*. The record's B side was 'I Talk to the Trees', sung by Clint Eastwood!

7 Sugar, honey and candy – just one chorus of the song would today exceed your daily recommended sugar intake.

8 In the song, Clive Dunn's 'Grandad' character reminisces not only about Charlie Chaplin, who 'made us laugh', but also about 'penny-farthings on the street', thereby making it sound as though his childhood lasted all the way from the 1870s to the 1910s.

9 'Ernie, the Fastest Milkman in the West' by Benny Hill. The tune was selected by David Cameron as one of his Desert Island Discs – who says politicians don't have any musical taste?

10 The song had first been used in a TV advert for Coca Cola, in which a group of the world's cleanest-looking hippies sang 'I'd Like to Give the World a Coke' on the side of a hill, as though attending a Woodstock-style festival that was entirely dedicated to fizzy drinks.

YOU KNOW YOU'RE 60 WHEN...

YOU STILL REGARD THINGS THAT HAPPENED IN THE 1970s AS RECENT EVENTS

The 1970s were simpler times. Back then, people took their time. They had no choice. It was very difficult walking fast in flared trousers and platform shoes. Leaving all that aside, see if you remember the following news stories from that particular decade.

1. Which position did Giovanni Montini, Albino Luciani and Karol Wojtyła all hold in 1978?

2. How did NASA try to introduce extra-terrestrials to the music of Bach, Mozart and Chuck Berry in 1977?

3. Which band appeared on Thames TV's *Today* programme, hosted by Bill Grundy, on 1 December 1976?

4. Which silent-film star died on Christmas Day 1977 and why was he back in the news three months later?

5. What children's favourite was added to the McDonald's menu in 1979?

6. What was the name of the Washington office complex where the US Democratic Party had their headquarters in 1972, and which has prompted the name of umpteen scandals since?

7   Elvis Presley died aged 42 on 16 August 1977. In which room of his home, Graceland, was he found?

8   Which male model claimed to have been the subject of a murder attempt instigated by Liberal Party leader Jeremy Thorpe in 1975?

9   What essential commodity was in short supply during the summer of 1976?

10 Who recited some words of St Francis of Assisi outside 10 Downing Street on 4 May 1979?

YOU KNOW YOU'RE 60 WHEN...

YOU STILL REGARD THINGS THAT HAPPENED IN THE 1970s AS RECENT EVENTS

— ANSWERS —

1   Pope. Giovanni Montini, who died in early August, was Paul VI. Albino Luciani was John Paul I, who died just 33 days after being elected. Karol Wojtyla became Pope John Paul II in October that same year. As a result, 1978 became known as the 'Year of the Three Popes', although they did not tour concert halls together like the Three Tenors.

2   Chuck Berry, Bach, Mozart, blues singer Blind Willie Johnson, plus words of greeting from US President Jimmy Carter and UN Secretary

General Kurt Waldheim, were included on a gold record sent into space on the unmanned craft *Voyager I*. We're still waiting for it to reach an alien civilisation with a vinyl record player.

3 The Sex Pistols. The person who repeatedly used four-letter words during the interview was guitarist Steve Jones, and also presumably the show's producer as he watched what was happening.

4 Charlie Chaplin died at Christmas 1977 and made an unwanted return to the world's headlines when his body was stolen and held to ransom the following year.

5 The Happy Meal. McDonald's decided to introduce their classic children's meal just when you became too old to have an excuse to try it.

6 Watergate. The ending '-gate' has since been added to other words to form the names of other scandals, including Camillagate, Sachsgate and, of course, the noise-pollution scandal Squeakygate.

7 Elvis was found on the toilet, not the most appropriate final throne for 'the King'.

8 Male model Norman Scott claimed that, following a gay relationship with Thorpe in the

1960s, the Liberal leader had hired a hitman to ensure the story didn't leak out. The alleged attempted murder sadly resulted in the death of Scott's Great Dane, Rinka.

9 Water – in the great drought of 1976, rivers and reservoirs across the UK ran dry. In late August, Denis Howell was appointed Minister for Drought. A few days later it began pouring with rain and Howell was appointed Minister of Floods instead (this really happened). Politicians had more of a sense of humour then.

10 Margaret Thatcher began her tenure as prime minister by quoting the text that began: 'Where there is discord, may we bring harmony.' Over the next 11 years, she frequently caused others to come out with religious exclamations as well.

YOU KNOW YOU'RE 60 WHEN...

YOU STILL CONVERT THE PRICES OF TODAY INTO 'OLD MONEY'

Being a 60-year-old now means you lived through decimalisation. You were taught all about one system of money, which was then abandoned. Ever since, you have been mentally converting prices into old money and exclaiming things like: '£1.30 a litre for petrol! That's five pounds and eighteen shillings a gallon!' But can you remember the decimal equivalents of the following old British coins and notes, what or who was depicted on them and when they were withdrawn from circulation?

1. Shilling
2. Old penny
3. Farthing
4. Halfpenny
5. Threepence
6. Sixpence
7. Florin
8. Half crown
9. Crown
10. Ten-shilling note

YOU KNOW YOU'RE 60 WHEN...

YOU STILL CONVERT THE PRICES OF TODAY INTO 'OLD MONEY'
— ANSWERS —

1. There were 20 shillings in a pound, so each shilling was the equivalent of the 5-new-pence piece introduced in 1968. The old shilling bore the English coat of arms, including the famous three lions, on its reverse side (all British coins, of course, display the reigning monarch on the front) and remained legal tender until 1990. At first the 5-new-pence coin had almost the same dimensions as the old shilling, but after 1990 it shrank to the tiny size it is today, which surely tells us something about the value of our money!

2 The old penny was a massive bronze coin (well, 31 mm across), with the image of Britannia on the reverse side. There were 12 pennies in a shilling and 240 pennies in a pound. The new decimal penny was therefore worth 2.4 old pennies, which was a bit of a headache to convert, so it was a good job the electronic calculator was introduced around the same time as decimalisation.

3 The farthing was worth a quarter of one old penny and would therefore have the monetary value today of dust. On the reverse side it had a wren, which, being a very small bird, was probably all they could fit on. It was withdrawn in 1960, so you probably don't remember it, unless you had very mean parents who continued to give you farthings in your pocket money.

4 The old halfpenny or ha'penny was, as its name suggests, half of one old penny, and it ceased to be legal tender in 1969. On the reverse side it depicted the *Golden Hind*, the ship in which Francis Drake circumnavigated the world. This was ironic, as you would not get far then or now on half a penny.

5 The old 'thrupenny' bit was worth three old pennies and had a Tudor portcullis on the reverse side. It ceased to be legal tender in 1971 but may now seem very valuable if you mistakenly look it up on the internet as a 'three penny bitcoin'.

6 The old silver sixpence was worth half a shilling, or 2.5 new pence, and was legal tender until 1980. It had a rose, shamrock, leek and thistle on the reverse, but you had to squint to see them as the coin was only slightly bigger than a 5p today.

7 The florin was a two-shilling coin, so there were ten of them in a pound, just like 10 new pence. That means we already had a decimal coin before decimalisation, but that didn't stop the government getting rid of our old money. The reverse side of the florin had the Tudor rose in the middle, surrounded by shamrocks, leeks and thistles. It remained in use until 1993, after which the 10-new-pence piece shrank to its present size.

8 The half crown was worth two shillings and sixpence (or 12.5p today) and had the Royal Coat of Arms on the reverse side. It was withdrawn from use in 1970.

9 A crown was worth 5 shillings (25p today) and also had the Royal Coat of Arms on the reverse side. Last minted as a five-shilling piece in 1965, it continues to be minted today for commemorative purposes, although its value was revised upwards to five pounds in 1990.

10 The 'ten-bob note' was reddish brown and the equivalent of 50p today. Britannia was depicted on the reverse side in the days before it was decided that banknotes should teach us about different figures from history and literature.

YOU KNOW YOU'RE 60 WHEN...

YOUR FAVOURITE READING MATTER IS REALLY STILL YOUR CHILDHOOD COMICS

Growing up without access to the internet meant that you were free from idle distractions and could spend your childhood reading morally and intellectually uplifting books. Or, perhaps more likely, your favourite comics. But do you remember in which comics you would have found the following characters?

1. Little Plum, Minnie the Minx, Roger the Dodger, Lord Snooty, The Bash Street Kids, Dennis the Menace and Gnasher, Biffo the Bear.

2. Korky the Cat, Desperate Dan, Keyhole Kate, Bully Beef and Chips, Corporal Clott.

3. Beryl the Peril, Danny's Tranny, Fred the Flop, Julius Cheeser, Tricky Dicky, Mickey the Monkey.

4. The Numskulls, Colonel Blink, The Smasher, The Badd Ladds, Baby Crockett, Ginger, The Banana Bunch.

5. Sid's Snake, Batty Bat, Odd Ball, Wear 'Em Out Wilf, Parker the Parky, Aqua Lad, Slowcoach, Champ.

6. Frankie Stein, Sweeny Toddler, Grimly Feendish, Sample Simon, Moana Lisa, Gal Capone.

7   Gus Gorilla, The Gasworks Gang,
Tomboy, Tricky Dicky, Ivor Lott and
Tony Broke, Whacky, Teacher's Pet.

8   The Four Marys, The Comp, 'Luv, Lisa',
Bella the Bookworm, Susan of Sunnysides.

9   Judge Dredd, Harlem Heroes, Dan Dare,
Robo-Hunter, Shako, The Visible Man.

10 Big Vern, the Pathetic Sharks, Felix and
his Amazing Underpants, The Brown
Bottle, Paul Whicker the Tall Vicar,
Johnny Fartpants, Buster Gonad and his
Unfeasibly Large Testicles.

YOU KNOW YOU'RE 60 WHEN...

YOUR FAVOURITE READING MATTER IS REALLY STILL YOUR CHILDHOOD COMICS

— ANSWERS —

1. *The Beano*, first published in July 1938 and still going today. But, of course, the glory years were when you used to get your copy to read every week!

2. *The Dandy*, which began in 1937 but is sadly no longer with us. If only you'd kept up your order with your local newsagent.

3. *The Topper*, another DC Thomson publication, like *The Beano* and *The Dandy*. Ceased publication in 1990.

4 *The Beezer*, again from the DC Thomson label. It absorbed *The Topper* in 1990, but itself only lasted another few years.

5 *Shiver and Shake*. A similar idea to Whizzer and Chips, but with a ghoulish, horror-tinged theme. This may have seemed appropriate in 1973, the year the film *The Exorcist* was released, but the comic was spirited away a year later.

6 *Shiver and Shake*. A similar idea to *Whizzer and Chips*, but with a ghoulish, horror-tinged theme. Presumably thought appropriate in the year *The Exorcist* was released, it first appeared in 1973 but was spirited away the following year.

7 *Cor!!* Issue one in 1970 came with ten free raspberry-flavoured drinks (in powdered form), while issue two had a whole piece of Anglo Bubbly bubble gum. Sadly, *Cor!!* was gone by 1974, causing people to exclaim: 'Cor! That didn't last long!'

8 *Bunty*. One of the few comics specifically for girls, this was again from comic supremos DC Thomson. It passed away to comic heaven in 2001.

9 *2000 AD*, the tough, action, sci-fi comic first published in 1977, when 2000 AD must have sounded like the far future, rather than, as we now remember it, the year of the Millennium Dome and Judith Keppel winning the jackpot on *Who Wants to be a Millionaire?*

10 *Viz Comic!* Just when you felt you were getting too old to buy comics, *Viz* appeared in Newcastle in 1979, went national in the 1980s and is still going today. So you can order it from your newsagent to be delivered with your weekly copy of *The Beano*!

YOU KNOW YOU'RE 60 WHEN...

YOU STILL LOVE COMEDY SHOWS FROM 40 OR 50 YEARS AGO

They say that you never laugh as much as when you were young. And that is definitely true for 60-year-olds, because you grew up watching some of the best-ever TV comedy shows on TV. Let's take a tour of classic and occasionally not-so-classic comedy from the 1960s and 1970s.

1. Which two 1970s sitcoms written by Jimmy Perry and David Croft were set during World War Two?

2. Which comedy series began in 1969 with a bearded man struggling up a beach and gasping 'It's ...'?

3. Which 1970s comedy threesome promised to do anything any time?

4. What was the name of the father-and-son rag-and-bone business in Shepherd's Bush?

5. Which series featured Jack Smethurst and Rudolph Walker living next door to one another and exchanging a stream of racially abusive terms?

6. What was the name of the hapless sitcom character married to Betty, played by Michele Dotrice?

7. Which couple lived next door to Jerry and Margo Leadbetter between 1975 and 1978?

YOU KNOW YOU'RE 60 WHEN...

YOU STILL LOVE COMEDY SHOWS FROM 40 OR 50 YEARS AGO

— ANSWERS —

1 *Dad's Army* (1968 to 1977) and *It Ain't Half Hot Mum* (1974 to 1981). *Dad's Army* repeats continue to make it one of the most-watched comedy shows on TV. *It Ain't Half Hot Mum*, with Michael Bates blacked up as Rangi Ram, is for some reason never repeated. Never mind, we can all remember every word of the theme tune ('Meet the gang 'cause the boys are here ...')

2 The bearded man was Michael Palin, who, apparently with his dying gasp, introduced *Monty Python's Flying Circus*, which ran from 1969 to 1974. And then forever afterwards as books, films, stage shows and West End musicals.

3 *The Goodies.* Between 1970 and 1982, long-time Python friends and associates Tim Brooke-Taylor, Graeme Garden and Bill Oddie battled with giant kittens, beanstalks, collapsing buildings and the ancient Lancastrian martial art of Ecky-Thump.

4 *Steptoe and Son.* Albert and Harold Steptoe and their horse Hercules plied their trade from Oil Drum Lane between 1962 and 1965 and again from 1970 to 1974.

5 *Love Thy Neighbour.* Another mysteriously little-repeated show, even though it ran for seven series between 1972 and 1976.

6 Frank Spencer, the disaster-prone, beret-and-raincoat-wearing central character of *Some Mothers Do 'Ave 'Em* between 1973 and 1978. Its theme tune was based on Morse code signals spelling out the show's title.

7 Tom and Barbara Good (Richard Briers and Felicity Kendal) converted their Surbiton home and garden into a self-sufficient mini-farm, to the bemusement and horror of their neighbours (played by Paul Eddington and Penelope Keith).

YOU KNOW YOU'RE 60 WHEN...

YOU STILL THINK THE FASHIONS OF THE 1960s AND 1970s LOOK GREAT

You may still regard the fashions of the 1960s and 1970s, when you were growing up, as the height of style and elegance, which is why you're still tempted to turn up to formal events in your beads, tie-dye shirt, platform shoes and purple loon pants. See if you can answer the following about the fashion scene of your youth.

1. Which road in Soho became famous in the 1960s for the clothes shops that attracted dedicated followers of fashion?

2. Which Welsh fashion designer began selling printed Victorian-style headscarves and went on to establish an international clothing and furnishing business?

3. Which women's fashion item took its name from a car first manufactured in 1959?

4. What name was coined for the very short shorts that became fashionable in the early 1970s?

5. What was the name of the London hairdresser famed for the 1960s bob cut and who opened his first chain of salons in the 1970s?

6. What was the essential item of footwear for glam rockers in the 1970s?

7   What was the name of the iconic 1960s fashion boutique opened in 1964 by Barbara Hulanicki?

8   Which Texan-born model appeared on the cover of Roxy Music's 1975 album *Siren*?

9   The 1966 film *Blow-Up* was inspired by the life of which fashion photographer, famed for his pictures of everyone from The Beatles to the Kray twins?

10   Which 16-year-old was 'the face of 1966' and was described by her boyfriend and manager Justin de Villeneuve as having 'a voice like a demented parrot'?

YOU KNOW YOU'RE 60 WHEN...

YOU STILL THINK THE FASHIONS OF THE 1960S AND 1970S LOOK GREAT

– ANSWERS –

1. Carnaby Street in London's West End. In the 1960s it was packed with independent boutiques such as Gear, Lady Jane, Lord John, I Was Lord Kitchener's Valet and a somewhat incongruous ironmonger's shop – presumably the hippest ironmonger in swinging London.

2. Laura Ashley. Mrs Ashley set up her first shop in that other renowned centre for fashion-crazed 1960s hipsters – Machynlleth in Wales!

3. The miniskirt was named after the Mini-Minor, and both of them were capable of causing traffic accidents.

4   Hot pants. Their creation, like that of the miniskirt, is often attributed to designer Mary Quant, who said her customers kept asking her to make her skirts 'shorter, shorter!' Presumably they also kept asking her to make her range of shorts 'tinier and more difficult to get into!'

5   Vidal Sassoon, who became world-famous for bestowing the bob cut on the stars of the day. Who Bob was, and what he thought of everyone nicking his haircut, is not recorded.

6   Platform shoes or boots were perfect for the outrageous styles and clod-hopping beats of glam rock. Not only that, they provided the likes of Elton John and Slade guitarist Dave Hill with a few much-needed extra inches of height!

7   Biba. This famous boutique was the place to go for miniskirts, floppy hats, tie-dye shirts and feather boas, as well as providing girls with an early excuse to shout to one other, 'Just in Biba!'

8   Jerry Hall appeared on Roxy Music's album cover. At the time she was dating lead singer Bryan Ferry, whom she left for Mick Jagger. She famously said, 'I prefer older men. I look better next to them.' She then went to extreme lengths to prove this by marrying Rupert Murdoch in 2016.

9 David Bailey, one of the great fashion photographers of the 1960s and beyond. His work helped establish some of the greatest models and style icons of the era. The Kray twins did not go on to have a successful modelling career, however.

10 Twiggy. Justin de Villeneuve, aka Nigel Davies, claimed to be responsible for Twiggy's success as 'the face of 1966', although her face surely belonged to her rather than him. Twiggy has since described him as 'my boyfriend who spent a lot of my money', and presumably she wasn't entirely thrilled by his 'demented parrot' line either.

YOU KNOW YOU'RE 60 WHEN...

YOUR CONVERSATION IS PEPPERED WITH CATCHPHRASES FROM DECADES AGO

Nothing will raise a smile and bring people together like dropping a well-known catchphrase into the conversation. Unfortunately, now you're 60, your favourite funny catchphrases are twice as old as most people you speak to. Never mind, can you complete or provide the responses to the following catchphrases? And who was famous for saying them?

1. 'Nice to see you, ...'

2. 'Are you free?'

3. 'I've started, so ...'

4. 'The cat's done a ...'

5. 'I didn't get where I am ...'

And what are the famous Morecambe and Wise responses to the following lines and situations?

6. André Previn telling Eric that he is playing all the wrong notes.

7. Eric hearing the sound of a police siren going past the window.

8. Eric asking, 'What do you think of it so far?'

9. Arthur Tolcher coming on to play his harmonica.

10. Ernie coughing.

YOU KNOW YOU'RE 60 WHEN...

YOUR CONVERSATION IS PEPPERED WITH CATCHPHRASES FROM DECADES AGO

— ANSWERS —

1 '... to see you nice!'

One of many from *The Generation Game*, featuring the king of catchphrases, Sir Bruce Forsyth. Others included 'Good game! Good game!', 'Give Us A Twirl,' and 'Didn't she/he/they do well?' Was there any part of the show that wasn't a catchphrase?

2 'I'm free!'

Mr Humphries' unforgettable response in *Are You Being Served?* To this day, whenever anyone asks you if you're free, you find it impossible to avoid replying in a sing-song 1970s camp voice.

3 '... I'll finish.'

A rare, non-comedic catchphrase from terrifying BBC quiz series *Mastermind*, hosted from 1972 to 1997 by Iceland-born Scot Magnus Magnusson. You now find yourself using it if you're speaking when a buzzer or fire alarm sounds, or if anyone interrupts you while you are eating a cake.

4 '... woopsy on the carpet.'

This is one of several phrases still trotted out today by people quoting Michael Crawford's Frank Spencer character in *Some Mothers Do 'Ave 'Em*. It may, however, only ever have been said once in the original series – which, astonishingly, is also the case with another of Frank's famous catchphrases: 'Oo, Betty!'

5 '... today by ...

Another adaptable catchphrase, originally trotted out by C.J. (John Barron) in *The Fall and Rise of Reginald Perrin*. Variations included 'I didn't get where I am today without making enemies' to 'I didn't get where I am today by drinking a liquid that's only been tested on pencils'.

6 'I'm playing all the right notes, but not necessarily in the right order.'

This famous interchange occurred when Eric attempted to perform Grieg's Piano Concerto under the guidance of LSO conductor André Previn, or 'Mr Preview' as Eric referred to him. Previn had already tried to get out of performing with him by saying he had to go and fetch his baton, which was in Chicago!

7 'He's not going to sell much ice cream going at that speed, is he?'

And this still works whenever an emergency vehicle passes by!

8 'Ruggish!'

Whenever Eric was standing next to a statue, or on one occasion holding a skull to recite Hamlet's soliloquy, he would turn to it and ask, 'What do you think of the show so far?'

9 'Not now, Arthur!'

Arthur Tolcher was a virtuoso harmonica player and old friend of Eric and Ernie from their days on the variety circuit, but he never got very far with his harmonica solos on their TV shows!

10 'Arsenal!'

Started in a sketch in which Eric played Mr Memory and the cough was used by Ernie to surreptitiously slip him the answer to a difficult football question. A similar technique was later used by Major Charles Ingram when he tried to win *Who Wants to be a Millionaire?*

YOU KNOW YOU'RE 60 WHEN…

YOU'RE SURPRISED TO FIND THAT THINGS YOU THOUGHT HAPPENED A YEAR AGO ACTUALLY HAPPENED IN THE 1980s

By the 1980s you had maybe left home, or perhaps you were at least being pushed towards the door by your parents. You had to start dealing with the world as an adult, even if no one else seemed to be doing that. So how much can you recall about the era when you came of age?

1. Rioting occurred in 1980 in St Pauls and in 1981 in Brixton, Toxteth, Moss Side, Handsworth and Chapeltown. But in which UK cities did these districts lie?

2. Which royal couples were married on 14 November 1973; 29 July 1981; 23 July 1986; 30 June 1978?

3. Which two British territories were invaded and occupied by Argentina in April 1982?

4. In December 1982, 30,000 women joined hands around Greenham Common Airbase. What were they protesting against?

5. Can you complete the following quote and identify who said it on 11 August 1984: 'My fellow Americans, I'm pleased to tell you today that I've signed legislation that will outlaw Russia forever ...'

6   Who were the leader of the National
    Union of Mineworkers and the
    chairman of the National Coal Board
    during the 1984/85 miners' strike?

7   By what name was the Community
    Charge introduced by the Conservative
    government in 1989 better known?

8   In 1986, the privatisation of which
    industry in the UK was advertised with
    the slogan, 'If you see Sid ... tell him!'

9   'Earlier on today, apparently, a woman
    rang the BBC and said she heard there
    was a hurricane on the way ... well, if
    you're watching, don't worry, there
    isn't.' Who said this on 15 October 1987
    and what happened shortly afterwards?

10 What was the name of the one-seater,
    three-wheeled electric vehicle launched
    in 1985?

YOU KNOW YOU'RE 60 WHEN...

YOU'RE SURPRISED TO FIND THAT THINGS YOU THOUGHT HAPPENED A YEAR AGO ACTUALLY HAPPENED IN THE 1980s

— ANSWERS —

1 St Pauls is in Bristol, Brixton in London, Toxteth in Liverpool, Moss Side in Manchester, Handsworth in Birmingham and Chapeltown in Leeds.

2 Princess Anne and Captain Mark Phillips married in November 1973; Charles and Diana married in July 1981; Andrew and Fergie married in July 1986; and Prince Michael of Kent married Baroness Marie Christine von Reibnitz in June 1978, although you may possess less souvenir tea towels and mugs commemorating that one!

3 The Falkland Islands and South Georgia and the South Sandwich Islands. A ceasefire was finally called in the Falklands on 14 June, and on 20 June the South Sandwich Islands were retaken, including an Argentine military base which had been there since 1976!

4 The deployment of US cruise missiles in the UK – the sort of cruise nobody wanted to book themselves onto.

5 '... We begin bombing in five minutes.' Ronald Reagan decided to have a little bit of fun while testing a microphone before a radio broadcast. Sticking with the more traditional 'Testing, one, two' might have involved less risk of precipitating nuclear conflict!

6 Arthur Scargill and Ian MacGregor respectively. Within 30 years of the strike, there were no deep coalmines left anywhere in the UK.

7 The 'poll tax', although some people called it other things which are too rude to be reprinted.

8 In ads for sales of British Gas shares, characters told each other, 'If you see, Sid ... tell him!' Sid is today believed to be living off the profits on his own personal tropical island, where he'll never need gas central heating again.

9 BBC weather forecaster Michael Fish made this announcement in October 1987. A few hours later the Great Storm of 1987 hit the UK. Another thing Michael Fish failed to predict was that we'd all still be going on about it more than 30 years later.

10 The Sinclair C5, which had a maximum speed of 15 mph, could go just 20 miles before it needed recharging and left you open to the elements. Designer Sir Clive Sinclair had previously produced the UK's first handheld electronic calculator, which he could have used to work out how much money he might lose on the C5!

YOU KNOW YOU'RE 60 WHEN...

YOU EXPECT TO HEAR THE DJs FROM YOUR YOUTH WHEN YOU SWITCH ON THE RADIO

When you were growing up, you could switch on the radio and listen to your favourite DJs cheerfully talking absolute nonsense. Today's DJs are, of course, still talking absolute nonsense, but unfortunately it's not a form of nonsense that anyone over the age of 30 can understand. So, instead, can you identify the following broadcasters from your youth?

1. Arnold the Dog's friend and the first DJ to broadcast on Radio 1 when it started.

2. The veteran Australian-born DJ known as 'Fluff'.

3. The Radio 1 DJ known as 'Diddy'.

4. The self-styled 'Hairy Cornflake'.

5. The veteran DJ and former singer, who was asked each day: 'What's the recipe today, Jim?'

6. The former Radio Caroline pirate DJ, who ran down the new singles chart on Radio 1 each Tuesday lunchtime.

7. The first female DJ to have her own show on Radio 1.

8. The presenter of *Junior Choice*.

9. The presenter of *The Perfumed Garden* on Radio London and *Top Gear* on Radio 1, and who appeared on *Top of the Pops* playing mandolin with Rod Stewart and the Faces.

YOU KNOW YOU'RE 60 WHEN...

YOU EXPECT TO HEAR THE DJs FROM YOUR YOUTH WHEN YOU SWITCH ON THE RADIO

— ANSWERS —

1 Tony Blackburn. Not only is Tony Blackburn still going from strength to strength himself, Arnold must be in the Guinness Book of Records as the world's longest-surviving dog.

2 Alan Freeman. Just the thought of him saying 'Greetings, pop pickers' starts his theme tune playing inside your head.

3. David Hamilton was the man who was unashamed for the world to know him as 'Diddy'.

4. Dave Lee Travis hosted the Radio 1 breakfast show in the late 1970s. And what more appetising concept could there be at breakfast time than a hairy cornflake?

5. Jimmy Young. Born in 1921, he was a chart-topping singer in the 1950s before becoming a Radio 1 DJ in 1967 and starting his 'JY prog' on Radio 2 in 1973. He finally said 'BFN – bye for now' – when he shuffled off this mortal coil in 2016 at the ripe old age of 95. Ironically, at no stage in his career was he particularly 'young'.

6. Johnnie Walker. If you were off school, you could tune in at lunchtime to hear him run down the brand new singles chart on Radio 1, although the poor signal made it like listening to something through a baked-bean tin on the end of a piece of string!

7. Annie Nightingale became the first woman Radio 1 DJ in 1969. It was such a successful experiment that Radio 1 decided to employ a second female DJ in the 1980s.

8 Ed Stewart, or 'Stewpot' as he was known, presented *Junior Choice* on Saturday and also hosted *Crackerjack* on TV, which meant that people shouted 'Crackerjack!' at him every time he left his house. On the plus side, he was never short of Crackerjack pencils.

9 John Peel, the legendary stalwart of Radio 1 from its beginning until his sadly premature demise in 2004. He was the irreplaceable purveyor of extraordinary groundbreaking new music, even if some listeners considered it to be unlistenable noise!

YOU KNOW YOU'RE 60 WHEN...

YOUR TASTE IN ALCOHOL WAS DEFINED IN THE 1970s

Alcohol, a substance you can enjoy once you're an adult to help you forget the problems of being an adult. As a 60-year-old, you may have started your drinking days in the late 1970s or early 1980s. If it was any earlier, it's not too late to hand yourself in to the police. Otherwise, let's take a wander through the alcoholic delights of your youth.

1   Which beer were we once told 'works wonders'?

2   Which lager refreshed the parts other beers couldn't reach?

3   Where was Lorraine Chase 'wafted here' from and what was she drinking?

4   Which brewer gave us the Party Seven and Red Label?

5   Which lager stayed sharp to the bottom of the glass?

6   Which was the pint that 'thinks it's a quart'?

7   Which lager was your best bet for a fuller flavour?

8   Can you complete the following slogan for beer: 'Smile please, ...'

9   Which lager was reassuringly expensive?

10   Which brand was 'probably the best lager in the world'?

YOU KNOW YOU'RE 60 WHEN...

YOUR TASTE IN ALCOHOL WAS DEFINED IN THE 1970s

— ANSWERS —

1 Double Diamond pale ale was the beer that was said to work wonders, which made it sound positively biblical!

2 Heineken made this claim of miraculous properties with a series of ads and posters presenting its restorative powers. They included Mr Spock's sagging ears becoming pointy again and a well-spoken young woman (played by Sylvestra Le Tousel) being transformed into full cockney as she said, 'The wa'er in Majorca don't taste like it wha' i' ough'er!'

3   In ads for Campari, Lorraine Chase was asked, 'Have you wafted here from paradise'? 'No, mate,' she replied, 'Luton Airport.' The adverts made her so successful, she might have been able to buy Luton Airport!

4   Watneys were the purveyors of Red Barrel and the Party Seven, which was a huge can containing seven pints. You could open one to have an instant party with six mates. Or a party on your own if you were feeling particularly thirsty.

5   Harp stayed sharp to the bottom of the glass, which was often more than the people drinking it managed.

6   Trophy Bitter, a liquid that clearly had delusions of grandeur. Apparently, the pint thought it was a quart because of all the foam that used to spill out over the top when it was poured.

7   Carling Black Label. The tag line on the adverts was 'I bet he drinks Carling Black Label'. Comedians Mark Arden and Stephen Frost appeared in various guises, including as RAF pilots launching bouncing bombs, which were deflected goalie-style by a German soldier, or sitting in the nuddy in a laundrette in a send-up of the Levi jeans ad.

8 '... You're in Greenall Whitley Land!' This may still be your automatic response every time a photographer asks you to 'smile, please'.

9 Stella Artois was advertised as being 'reassuringly expensive', which was a better way of making its price sound like a positive thing than saying: 'Stella Artois. Blimey! Have you seen how much they charge you for this stuff?'

10 Carlsberg. The exact mathematical nature of this probability was, however, never given.

YOU KNOW YOU'RE 60 WHEN...

PEOPLE THINK THEY'VE GONE BACK IN TIME WHEN THEY SEE YOUR HOME DECOR

Our ancestors would not recognise many of the things we have in our houses today. And your grandchildren may not recognise some of your possessions from the 1970s and 1980s. How many of the following do you remember, or maybe even still possess?

1. What must-have item of 1970s home decoration involved a light bulb, a blob of wax and a transparent liquid?

2. Which executive toy of the 1970s and 1980s was named after a seventeenth-century scientist?

3. One of the first domestic items sold by Habitat from 1964 onwards was referred to as a continental quilt. What do we call it today?

4. Digital watches first appeared in the 1970s. What sort of crystal were we regularly told they contained?

5. Which financial services product was advertised in the 1970s as being 'your flexible friend'?

6. Which variety of kitchen appliance was marketed in 1974 by the Australian company Breville?

7   C60, C90 and C120 were the most common varieties of which audio product?

8   Which kitchen utensil became a bestseller for Habitat in the 1960s despite being previously largely unknown in the UK, and was later described by food writer Elizabeth David as 'ridiculous and pathetic'?

9   What was the name of the trading stamps given out to customers by Tesco supermarkets, petrol stations and other retailers between 1958 and 1991?

10 Which two competing forms of video-recording equipment were launched by JVC and Sony in the late 1970s?

YOU KNOW YOU'RE 60 WHEN...

PEOPLE THINK THEY'VE GONE BACK IN TIME WHEN THEY SEE YOUR HOME DECOR

— ANSWERS —

1. The lava lamp. The light bulb heated up the wax, which then floated up and down in entertainingly shaped blobs. And what more relaxing concept is there than molten lava?

2. The Newton's cradle, a row of little metal balls hanging from a frame which you could set clacking against one another. This is what people in offices spent their days staring at in the days before the internet!

3 A duvet. Habitat used to advertise it by saying it only took ten seconds to make your bed. They didn't mention that every few days you had to spend an hour holding it upside down and shaking it to get all the stuffing back from the bottom end!

4 Quartz. Digital watches contained a piece of quartz crystal, which vibrated at precisely 32,768 times per second when an electric current was passed through it – at least until the battery ran out and you had to prise the back off your watch with a penknife.

5 The Access credit card was marketed as 'your flexible friend', which made it sound like a particularly accommodating contortionist.

6 The sandwich toaster. Also known as the 'Breville Thing in the Back of the Kitchen Cupboard We Bought 20 Years Ago, But Only Used Once'.

7 These were the most common formats of audio cassette, their designations corresponding to the number of minutes you could record on them for (e.g. you could record for 60 minutes on a C60). In the 1970s and 1980s, we were warned that home-taping on cassettes was killing the music industry. Mainly they seemed to do this by spilling tape all over the place, forcing you to wind it back in using a pencil!

8 The garlic press. Every home has one now, but back in the 1960s and 1970s garlic seemed to be despised and feared. Maybe British men of the time were prejudiced because they still remembered being at war with the sort of people who ate the stuff!

9 Green Shield Stamps. Your parents got one for every 6d that they spent and then had to spend hours sticking them into a collecting book. In fact, they probably had you do that for them. In 1965, Green Shield Stamps offered a motorboat for 170 books (equivalent to £5,440 worth of shopping) or a gent's brush-and-comb set for one book (equivalent to £32 worth of shopping).

10 JVC produced the VHS video while Sony produced the Betamax. In the battle for supremacy, VHS eventually came out on top, which means that proud VHS owners today have more useless old videos stacked up in their attics than anyone else.

YOU KNOW YOU'RE 60 WHEN...

THE SOUNDTRACK TO YOUR LIFE IS THE SOUNDTRACK OF THE FILMS YOU GREW UP WATCHING

As a 60-year-old, some of the greatest movies ever made were released during your lifetime and you had the opportunity to watch them while stuffing yourself with Cornettos and popcorn before anyone else. But in which films of your youth did the following pieces of music feature?

1. 'Windmills of Your Mind' (1968)
2. 'Also sprach Zarathustra' (1968)
3. 'Born to Be Wild' (1969)
4. 'The Entertainer' (1973)
5. *Tubular Bells* (1973)
6. 'You're the One That I Want' (1978)
7. 'The Ride of the Valkyries' (1979)
8. 'Eye of the Tiger' (1982)
9. 'Up Where We Belong' (1982)
10. 'Take My Breath Away' (1986)

YOU KNOW YOU'RE 60 WHEN...

THE SOUNDTRACK TO YOUR LIFE IS THE SOUNDTRACK OF THE FILMS YOU GREW UP WATCHING

— ANSWERS —

1 Performed by Noel Harrison (son of Rex) and used in the cool crime caper *The Thomas Crown Affair*. The song won the Academy Award for best original song in 1968. The previous year's winner had been 'Talk to the Animals', sung by Noel's dad.

2 Richard Strauss's orchestral tone poem was used as the theme for Stanley Kubrick's sci-fi classic *2001 A Space Odyssey* and was adopted for TV coverage of the following year's Moon landings and as Elvis's concert walk-on music.

3 *Easy Rider*. The gritty road movie about a pair of drug dealers riding across the USA on Harley Davidsons probably provided the musical soundtrack for you as you rode around outside your house on your Raleigh Chopper bike. Steppenwolf sang this particular track.

4 Scott Joplin's ragtime piano compositions were used in *The Sting*, in which Robert Redford and Paul Newman play a pair of grifters attempting to pull the con of a lifetime on a big-time crime boss. Having died in 1917, Joplin unfortunately missed out on the royalties.

5 William Friedkin's terrifying horror *The Exorcist* used the opening from Mike Oldfield's *Tubular Bells*. The film would have had a very different feel if they had instead used 'The Sailor's Hornpipe' that features on side two.

6 This was the classic number-one hit from *Grease*, with John Travolta and Olivia Newton John each wearing a pair of trousers so tight they even distracted you from John Travolta's singing.

7   Wagner's theme accompanied the helicopter attack in Francis Ford Coppola's *Apocalypse Now*. In a separate scene, Robert Duvall proclaims 'I love the smell of napalm in the morning.' Despite this recommendation, you should never try using it as an aftershave lotion.

8   *Rocky III*, the one featuring Mr. T as boxer Clubber Lang saying, 'I pity the fool.' The video for the theme tune featured the band Survivor walking together down an urban street looking tough, apart from the slightly podgy one in glasses, who seemed to be stomping along using invisible walking sticks.

9   *An Officer and a Gentleman*. The film starred Richard Gere, as an officer, and Debra Winger, who presumably played a gentleman. The song was performed by Joe Cocker and Jennifer Warnes.

10 Performed by Berlin and used in the Tom Cruise film *Top Gun*. The tune has also been used to advertise cars but, inexplicably, not mouthwash.

YOU KNOW YOU'RE 60 WHEN...

THE MOST RECENT POP MUSIC YOU LIKE IS FROM THE 1970s AND EARLY 1980s

Being 60, the soundtrack to some of the most significant moments in your life was supplied by some of the most bizarre-looking and strangely dressed individuals to have ever lived. See if you can identify the following.

1   Which artist has had number ones
    during your lifetime as part of a quintet
    and a quartet in the 1960s, as part of a
    trio in the 1970s, and as part of a duo
    and as a solo artist in the 1980s?

2   Which group's hits told the stories of
    'Russia's greatest love machine' and
    'Mary's Boy Child Jesus Christ'?

3   Which bestselling 1978 album featured
    Justin Hayward, David Essex, Phil
    Lynott and Richard Burton?

4   The title of which 1977 punk album was
    thought to be so obscene it had to be
    defended in court by John Mortimer?

5   Which soundtrack LP released in 1978
    featured the Bee Gees, Yvonne Elliman,
    KC and the Sunshine Band and a disco
    version of Beethoven's Fifth Symphony?

6 Which six characters are named in Queen's 1975 Christmas number one 'Bohemian Rhapsody'?

7 Which song by The Specials hit number one in the summer of 1981 around the time of rioting in Liverpool, Leeds, Birmingham and Manchester?

8 Which Frankie Goes To Hollywood number-one hit featured excerpts from the UK government's nuclear war information film 'Protect and Survive'?

YOU KNOW YOU'RE 60 WHEN...

THE MOST RECENT POP MUSIC YOU LIKE IS FROM THE 1970s AND EARLY 1980s

— ANSWERS —

1. Paul McCartney. 'Get Back' was credited to The Beatles and Billy Preston (so a quintet); The Beatles had a few numbers ones themselves; Wings topped the charts as a trio with 'Mull of Kintyre' in 1977, the 'year of punk'; and Macca returned to the top spot in the 1980s on his own and on duets with Stevie Wonder and Michael Jackson. And that's not even mentioning his work with the Frog Chorus!

2 Boney M had hits with 'Rasputin' and 'Mary's Boy Child'. If you are studying Russian history, listening to the works of Boney M is not an adequate form of revision. For a start, Rasputin's first name wasn't really Ra-ra.

3 *Jeff Wayne's Musical Version of War of the Worlds*, which retold the story of the H. G. Wells novel. Despite the album being hugely successful, he did not then work through all H. G. Wells' other works, so sparing the world Jeff Wayne's *Musical Version of Tono-Bungay* and *Jeff Wayne's Musical Version of Anticipations of the Reactions of Mechanical and Scientific Progress upon Human Life and Thought*.

4 *Never Mind the Bollocks, Here's the Sex Pistols*. Following the arrest of a record-shop owner in Nottingham for displaying the LP, barrister and *Rumpole of the Bailey* author Mortimer successfully argued that calling the ancient word 'bollocks' obscene was a load of... nonsense.

5 *Saturday Night Fever*. As well as a disco version of Beethoven's 5th, the album also included a disco arrangement of Russian composer Mussorgsky's 'Night on the Bare Mountain'. Beethoven's and Mussorgsky's work had never previously appeared on a record with the Bee Gees bearing their chests on the cover.

6   Galileo, Figaro, Scaramouche, Beelzebub,
    Bismillah and ... Mama! 'Bohemian Rhapsody'
    is sometimes said to have been the first
    music video, although let's not forget the
    accompanying film for Benny Hill's 'Ernie (The
    Fastest Milkman in the West)' four years earlier.

7   'Ghost Town', an eerie and dramatic reflection
    of the times, although slightly less suitable for
    use at parties or to accompany funerals.

8   'Two Tribes'. The video featured a wrestling
    bout, supposedly between US President
    Ronald Reagan and Soviet leader Konstantin
    Chernenko. The actor Patrick Allen supplied
    the voice-over from 'Protect and Survive',
    having previously performed voice-over duties
    on a great many films, including *Carry On... Up
    the Khyber*.

YOU KNOW YOU'RE 60 WHEN...

YOU NEED TO LOOK UP THE ANSWERS TO THE FOLLOWING QUESTIONS ON THE INTERNET

You've reached 60 and that means you've lived to an age where you have access to the internet. And thanks to that fact you can look up the answers to the following vital questions about your life which would have left previous generations scratching their heads.

1 What was the number one record in the charts the week that you were born?

2 What were the main news headlines on the day you entered the world?

3 Who were the Prime Minister, Chancellor of the Exchequer, Home Secretary and Foreign Secretary at the time?

4 What was the weather like on the day you were born?

5 What were the top films at the box office that week?

6 What was on TV that evening?

7 Which celebrities were born on the same day as you?

8 Which famous people died around the time you were born?

9 What was the population of the world the day you were born?

10 How much did a loaf of bread, a pint of milk and a gallon of petrol cost?

FILL IN YOUR ANSWERS BELOW

1

2

3

4

5

6

7

8

9

10

If you're interested in finding out more about our books, find us on Facebook at Summersdale Publishers and follow us on Twitter at @Summersdale.

www.summersdale.com